G000123560

PUDD'N
THE CAT
FROM A CARDBOARD BOX

BY JOYCE STEVENS-SMITH

First Edition published 2009 by
2QT Limited (Publishing)
Dalton Lane, Burton In Kendal
Cumbria LA6 1NJ
www.2qt.co.uk

Printed in Great Britain by the MPG Books Group, Bodmin and King's Lynn

Mixed Sources

Product group from well-managed
forests, controlled sources and
recycled wood or fiber
www.fsc.org Cert no. TT-COC-002303
© 1996 Forest Stewardship Council

FSC

All profits arising from the sale of this book will be donated to suitable charities

Additional cover images supplied by istockphoto.com & Peter Miidenhall
Cover design Robbie Associates

A CIP catalogue record for this book
is available from the British Library
ISBN 978-0-9562368-2-1

For William and Emily and all cat lovers.

Foreword

Over the years that these photographs were taken, Pudd'n was always considered a character. From his uncertain beginnings and his longevity, I felt his story was worth telling. Not having a mother cat to show him how to behave, he would imitate human behaviour on many occasions, and touched so many people's lives.

To friends and relatives who 'cat sat' when I was away on holiday, I say a big Thank You. My visitors from around the world, and sailing friends who knew and enjoyed him in his sailing days, would always enquire about him in letters, phone calls and latterly emails.

Acknowledgements

Most of the photographs were taken by me, however I would like to acknowledge and thank;

Peter Mildenhall for the cover photograph of Pudd'n.

Vivienne Taylor for the photograph of Nimrod and others with the Royal Yacht Britannia.

The drawing of Pudd'n chasing the butterflies, was kindly done by Lucy Turpitt.

The lovely Prayer is by Nina Hinchy.

Iris Bennett and Rosalee Pope for kindly reading the drafts and offering suggestions and corrections and,

My grateful thanks to Kevin Benjamin, who gave of his time and knowledge with the photographs and text for the original booklet.

A CHINESE CAT FROM CAUSEWAY BAY TO CAWSAND

Ah Wong's Mission

The box was perched unsteadily on Ah Wong's lap, the contents agitated by the noise of the tram and smells wafting up through the windows from the adjacent market, of vegetables, meats and fish, some of it not so fresh. Ah Wong's thoughts were on the forthcoming horse race meeting at Happy

Hong Kong Tram

Valley and the luck he was going to have backing the winner. A sudden jolt as the tram stopped, he pushed his way through the sweating passengers and alighted at the waters edge of Causeway Bay, where he deposited the box and without a backward glance, made his way to the Jockey Club and the racing...

THE BEGINNING

Mine

From the confines of the box I struggled and fell into open space. Suddenly strong hands took hold of me and the smell of man engulfed me.

Where I was found 'X' marks the spot!

Partial view of causeway and The Royal Hong Kong Yacht Club

What was to happen next I did not know but the warmth of the man's jacket pocket gave me comfort.

My Family

The lunch time session at the Yacht Club Bar was in full voice. Eric made his way to the telephone, two urgent calls to make.

One to the RSPCA, to tell them of a box with five kittens on an area near the Noon Day Gun causeway, the next to his wife.

"Can we have a cat?"

Joyce replied, "Is it fair to the animal when we are at work all day and sailing at weekends?"

"We will take him with us," was the reply.

EARLY DAYS

Later the Vet having passed the little thing no more than five weeks old, the bundle of fluff was fed with a pipette and a little butter smeared on his paws.

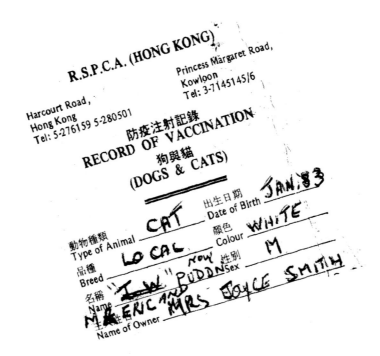

My Life

Somehow I understood that I was to lick, and my owners realised I was a white kitten and not dirty grey. Their obvious delight at this encouraged me to wash more vigorously.

After the cardboard box the area of this room seemed enormous. I had food, warmth and love, in return I would purr and snuggle onto any available lap.

Exploring the area was fun and a game of paper ball was a great exercise. I was considered very clever at fetching and carrying it back to Master and Missee alternating as each threw it across the room.

I suddenly found I had a name ... 'Time waster' or 'TW', as each evening was spent in this activity. I continued this game over many years, but sadly there was to come a time when Master and I were unable to play this.

NEW HORIZONS

Time does not mean a great deal to a kitten but seemingly the days passed and I began to grow on my diet of fish, rice and water.

Then came the day when I was to broaden my horizons.

I was placed into a special basket and very apprehensively refused to settle until my cosy blanket was placed beside me.

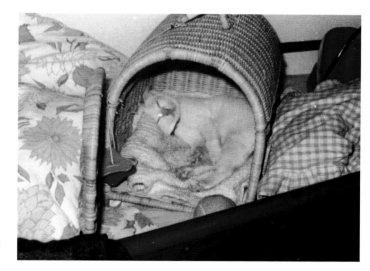

Once again I was lifted up and continued to voice my protest as the noise of the engine gave me a flash back to that other journey.

We passed the vets house and as we stopped I heard the noise of what I was to know as wind. This time there was no cardboard box but the chug of a sampan and again I found myself in a strange area.

"This is **'Nimrod'** Pusscat", (my second name change), said Eric. "You are going sailing."

After a great deal of noise and activity I snuggled up in my basket where I tried to sleep, suddenly engines ceased and all was quiet except for a gentle swishing sound which I was later to understand was wind in sails and the sea passing the ships hull. I became very accustomed to these surroundings and the motion of the yacht.

In fact my cosy place in the pilot berth was very comfortable.

Suddenly I realised that I was at a different angle and had to dig my claws in to stay in one position.

When I heard activity I knew I should move. In fact my Master would call out, 'We are going to tack' and I would climb out of the bunk and get into the pilot berth on the other side. These people called them Port and Starboard.

Seemingly I had found my sea legs and when all was quiet I ventured on deck. Gone were the smells and noise of a busy Hong Kong. This was very peaceful and I discovered that this was being at anchor. I was then introduced to all the buddy boats and as the weeks went by I would visit each one and receive a great welcome.

Even at night it was a joy to walk the deck. Amazing to see a moon on the water, the occasional flying fish and snuggling up to Master's (who slept on deck)

sleeping bag, it was so peaceful ...

... and my Master would say, "Amazing to think that across the Bay and over the hills there are 5 million people and we are lucky to be enjoying this."

Moments Afloat

When the North East monsoon started to blow at times it became very uncomfortable and I enjoyed another experience. All yachts would go to pontoons at the Shelter Cove Club. I was allowed to walk along this but I wasn't too keen on this as again it conjured up the memory of being in a cardboard box. Compensation for this was being taken to the Club House and curling up beside a log fire. This was bliss.

CHRISTMAS PUDD'N

Christmas on board was fun and provided so much
attention and
excitement . . .

Presents...

Turkey...

... that a sleep was
necessary after
sampling a little
turkey.

Nap...   Happy Christmas!

OPERATION ... AND AT HOME

I had two operations in my life and after one of these I found it difficult to eat with a special collar on but it only lasted a few days.

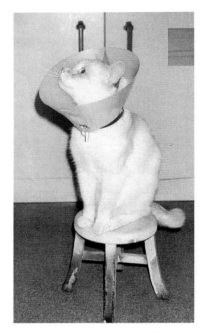

After my operation, so that I did not father kittens, I tended to put on weight and my undercarriage would sway in the breeze.

A friendly 'yachtie' said I was just like a pudding.

Master would not have this and said, "He is more dignified than that he shall be called **P.U.D.D. apostrophe 'N'**," and that was to be my name for all my time although as you will see I do acquire other nicknames.

This happy existence persisted for many years and as soon as I saw the red sail bag at the door I knew it was boat time.

Preparing my fish ...

Hope on hope ever ...

Just waiting ...

Cleaning - and waiting ...

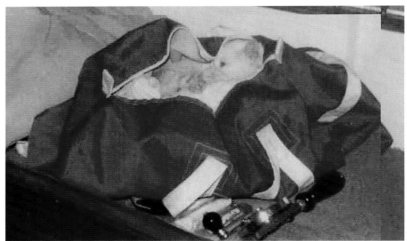

A favourite place ...

MORE OF MY YEARS BEFORE THE MAST

Waiting for everybody to get ready

I remember many visitors on board making a fuss of me and I did so enjoy visiting other boats, especially inspecting their galleys. On one yacht, when seated on the navigation table, I was fascinated by a small light whizzing around a screen. I later understood that this was a satellite system and so I acquired another nickname into the bargain -**'CatNav'**.

Some of the friends I visited and a raft up of Buddy boats at Dai Sai Wan

I preferred being at anchor to the actual sailing, especially when it was rough, but I was never seasick.

Then one day I nearly lost one of my nine lives. We were at anchor I jumped into our dinghy. **I was in charge and Captain Cat,** until I tried to leap back on board from the edge of the dinghy.

I did not appreciate the law of action and reaction, and as I leapt the dinghy went backwards from under me and in I went into the sea. I meowed loudly and used my paws to stay afloat till master came and rescued me.

I was given a fresh water shower on the foredeck. Missee said that there was nothing quite so funny as a showered cat.

Deck work for the crew

Are we really going round the Ninepins in this weather?

Pulling on the sheets

What a bunch of knitting ...

Some days my whiskers would twitch and my fur feel sticky, so I would climb on top of the refrigerator into a bag—this felt safe.

Especially when my Master would say with a chuckle, "Its enough to blow his whiskers off" (not dogs off chains). We did not venture out and the flat was full of noise...

It was a typhoon!

Comfortable Places

If he says 'tack' once more ...

... I'll go back to my bunk!

On

And...

Off Watch

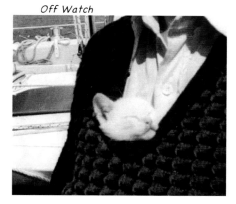

27

*Not sure if this was a bedtime story, but it was **very** cosy!*

ROYAL OCCASION

One day my fur was given a special brush and a new red collar put on. Why was this happening, was I going to be sold? My worries did not subside.

Off we went to 'Nimrod' and with several other Royal Hong Kong Yacht Club Yachts sailed out into the harbour. A great deal of activity then took place on board. We were being dressed 'overall' in honour of the passage of the Royal Yacht Britannia.

HK fireboat, RHKYC yachts (Highland Fling and Nimrod) with Royal Yacht Britannia

29

Master insisted I sport an extra collar, a blue one. I was carried on deck looking very patriotic with my white fur and red and blue collars. There was much cheering and sounding of ship hooters. I was held aloft in Master's arms as Britannia sailed past, after all, a Cat can look at a Queen. I was not to know then that I was to see this graceful ship again in my lifetime, albeit in sadder circumstances.

When the Queen was ashore and outside the City Hall, my Missee said, "Welcome to Hong Kong ma 'am," and as the Queen graciously turned round my Missee took this picture.

Her Majesty Queen Elizabeth II with the Hong Kong Governor, Sir Edward Youde

Sadly the Governor died suddenly whilst on a visit to Beijing in December 1986. As you will see later, it was on the same day my master had equally devastating news.

HELPING OTHERS

One weekend in the 80's a good breeze saw us through the harbour and Lei Yue Mun gap, across Joss House Bay, paying homage to goddess 'Queen of Heaven' Tin Hau, the Taoist pantheon and the protector of sea faring folk at Joss House Temple on the way.

Once through Fat Tong Mun we headed north but the wind began to die and as we approached Steep Island we decided to motor sail.

Just ahead of us was a traditional mainland fishing junk in full sail, trying to make headway in limited breeze.

My first thoughts were of pirates and I was scared,

Oh dear, was I going to end up in a stew pot?

Naturally we began to overtake them. As we did so a waft of a fish smell reached my nostrils. Two smiling Chinese stood on the foredeck brandishing a rope and gesturing.

Missee said to Master "They are asking for a tow."

Eric, always ready to help another sailor, agreed.

Our own rope was found should it be required and we took them in tow.

I wasn't too keen on the yapping thing on the deck, which my Master said was a Chow dog.

It was evident from their actions and my Masters limited Cantonese that they were interested in what we were drinking. Their delight was plain to see when six cans of cold San Miguel were thrown to them. At Bluff Island they indicated to us they would anchor there to await tide and a more favourable wind. As we let the line go there was much bowing, shaking of hands and 'daw jeh' (thank you) 'daw jeh' (thank you). Thankfully the dog did not come on deck.

We continued on to our overnight anchorage in Dai Sai Wan. Unknown to us our exploits had been noted by fellow 'yachties' and all agreed Eric and 'Nimrod' had gained great kudos with the Chinese fishing folk. It was possibly good insurance ready for the handover in 1997.

SADNESS AND NEW SURROUNDINGS

Sadly my Master was never to put this to the test, as you will see, there came a day in 1986 when all this came to an end. People came to the house but we did not go to the boat. Visitors came and the word cancer was heard, I wasn't sure what this meant.

Master was at home all day and I would spend time with him in the workshop, sometimes he could not pick me up or wish me to snuggle on his lap.

Then it all seemed different, he did not seem to be around, my special friend had left me.

Joyce would cuddle me and talk sadly about missing Eric. I too felt this, as he had saved me those many years ago from a certain death but I could not save him…

I would sit in his workshop but there was no noise of a drill or smell of wood shavings or oil. Familiar things were gone. I felt angry and lost.

I was fed and loved and came to understand that the lovely things we had enjoyed were special memories, the sadness was in the house but slowly the sun began to shine again.

I taste dried food I.A.M.s

37

Missee and I had to move house and I had to get used to new surroundings. I had many new friends to make a fuss of me and Joyce had a small area with several plants.

I discovered Lemon grass and chives, which I loved to chew.

Guarding my Lemon Grass

The days passed but sadly the boat days were finished.

In my 10th year I knew that great things were being planned. I did not always understand the words my Missee said and what it was to mean, "going away", "new life", "long journey", "but we will be together again in a **lovely place**."

Missee cuddled me and I licked her wet face which tasted of salt.

Again I was lifted up, not in a cardboard box but a cushioned basket with my own blanket and favourite pussycat granules. So many noises and smells.

The motion was so strange, thankfully I was cosy and fell asleep.

ANOTHER WORLD

Time means nothing to a contented cat. I think I slept a long time. Again I was lifted out with kindly hands.

"Welcome to England, Pudd'n," said the man. I guess I was taken to a car and it seemed a long time in this, not the short journey I had when going to the boat.

I was then in a little room with my own penny box, bed, food tray and a special tree that I could scratch at and climb.

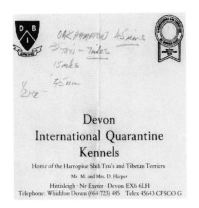

Devon
International Quarantine
Kennels

Home of the Harropine Shih Tzu's and Tibetan Terriers

Mr. M. and Mrs. D. Harper

Hittisleigh · Nr Exeter · Devon EX6 6LH

Telephone: Whiddon Down (064 723) 485   Telex 45643 CFSCO G

This was **QUARANTINE!**

I had many people seeing me, and they were full of admiration that I had come all the way from Hong Kong. In fact I was well cared for and made to feel very special.

Suddenly one day I was picked up and familiar feelings and smells overwhelmed me.

Missee carried me out for yet another car journey.
Then the car stopped.

"This is the **lovely place**," said Missee.

The basket was opened and my joy was complete when I wandered around and found my old favourite chairs and cushions.

Chow time

My favourite stool

This was my English home.

The days were spent
familiarising myself with all the
new things.

We were happy, I was allowed outside in a place called 'garden and grounds'.

I met other people and was called 'Chinese Charlie'.

I also had my first meeting with 'Lady Em', the cat next door.
We would have conversations but would keep our distance. I had marked my territory.

I suddenly found the exhilaration of chasing butterflies in the long grass. They were too quick for me but it was fun.

One day out on the hill it felt very cold and wet and I lost my feet when I walked.

Gosh! This was Snow!!

I lose my feet ...

When it was very cold, to snuggle on the carpet next to the fire, was bliss.

Christmas time again

I must have a present in here
somewhere ...

Perhaps its only pussycat
aranules. and not TOYS ...

Favourite places

The wall of the Fort was my favourite position, and a scene to remind me of my own sailing days. I know my master would have loved it here.

Looking out over the village towards the Devon coastline

My other view on a very misty day was of the Royal Yacht Britannia sailing across Cawsand Bay, during her last voyage around the UK after the sad decommissioning.

I, like my Missee, shed a tear both remembering treasured memories of the happy time when we last saw her.

22 10 '97

Royal Yacht Britannia 1997

Another famous ship seen in the Bay was a replica of
Captain Cooks 'Endeavour', the original of which sailed from
Plymouth in 1768

Eleven years here passed with happiness and contentment.

When it was very hot I would sit under a bush or on a seat beside Missee who would enjoy a cup of tea.

SLOWING DOWN

I did not even mind my yearly visit to the vet for a check up. I did not enjoy the car journey but once there I was much admired by the staff, especially when they knew of my advancing age and that I came from Hong Kong and my Missee told of my sailing exploits.

In my advancing years I acquired more ginger fur — unlike humans who seem to go grey.

I also managed to get to grips with at least a part of 21st Century technology.

Computer Cat – the mouse fortunately survived

MY LAST DAYS

In my 21st year I knew I was slowing down, although I could eat and drink I did have times when I could not control my movements.

Then one day my back legs would not allow me to walk.

I curled up happily in my favourite place musing on my interesting and momentous life of 21 years and 6 months.

From such a disadvantaged beginning and my own struggle of crawling out of that cardboard box into the unknown.

Then the finding of a loving family and friends whom I in return loved and became the peoples Pussycat . . . showed all things are possible if one makes an effort.

My Missee talked to me, gently held my paw and I closed my eyes and dreamt of Pussy heaven, and the vet let me go to sleep.

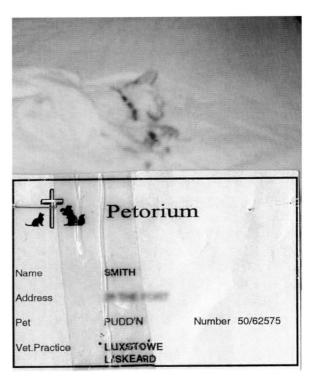

Footnote -Pudd's ashes are buried under a bush he loved in the garden in Cawsand, where Joyce lives. Joyce sent a small amount to Hong Kong, where friends kindly took them to Jade Bay, Sai Kung, a favourite anchorage for 'Nimrod' and crew, where Eric's ashes were scattered in 1987.

A PRAYER FOR PUDD'N AND ALL ANIMALS

By courtesy of Nina Hinchy

Dear Lord Jesus,

Our little cat has died.

We cried because he was so loving and good.

He made everyone happy.

We are glad it's you who've got him now.

Please take care of him, of course you will

You love all animals, you made them all.

Thank you for letting us have him first,

And for all the happy times we had with him.

AMEN.

Where Pudd'n lived –

The twin villages of Kingsand and Cawsand

The tapestry was worked by residents and visitors under the direction of a team of skilled needle-women

This is a photograph of a large tapestry that was worked for the Millennium celebrations – and clearly visible (at the point marked by the red circle) in the original are two white stitches on the wall of the old Fort, that symbolized Pudd'n on his favourite viewpoint.

About the Author

Joyce Stevens first drew breath at the General Lying In Hospital off the Waterloo Road, London and it was at this same hospital some years later that she passed her final Midwifery examination. In 1962, following duties in the operating theatres and casualty, and a sad romance she set off first to Gibraltar on a 4 year contract, then in 1967 a sea journey and a nursing opportunity at The Matilda and War Memorial Hospital Hong Kong. Hong Kong was to be her home for the next 26 years. Offshore sailing was to become one of her passions and after participating in many races including the bi annual China Sea Race she became a member of the Royal Ocean Racing Club.

New dimensions were added to her life in 1975. The most important was her marriage in the spring to engineer Eric Smith. They shared the passion of the sea and the autumn saw the launch of their sloop 'Nimrod' which they sailed every weekend except during typhoons.

Pudd'n the cat, rescued from a cardboard box was added to the crew in January 1983.

Whilst nursing in Hong Kong she researched and had published a book about the hospital and the life of the Victorian lady it was named after, who was resident in Hong Kong 1858 – 1893.

October 1975 saw the first Matilda Hospital Sedan Chair Race, inspired and organised by Joyce, in aid of Hong Kong Charities. The Race continues to this day and over 40 Million HK Dollars has been raised for many deserving causes.

Following Eric's untimely death from Cancer in 1987, Joyce became a keen fundraiser in the promotion of hospice care and the building of Hong Kong's first hospice. The Bradbury Hospice was opened by HRH Prince Charles in 1992.

Retirement beckoned and in 1993 Joyce returned to England,to Cawsand, Cornwall and an involvement in village life. Pudd'n joining her after his 6 months quarantine.